STARS

Strategies

To

Achieve

Reading

Success

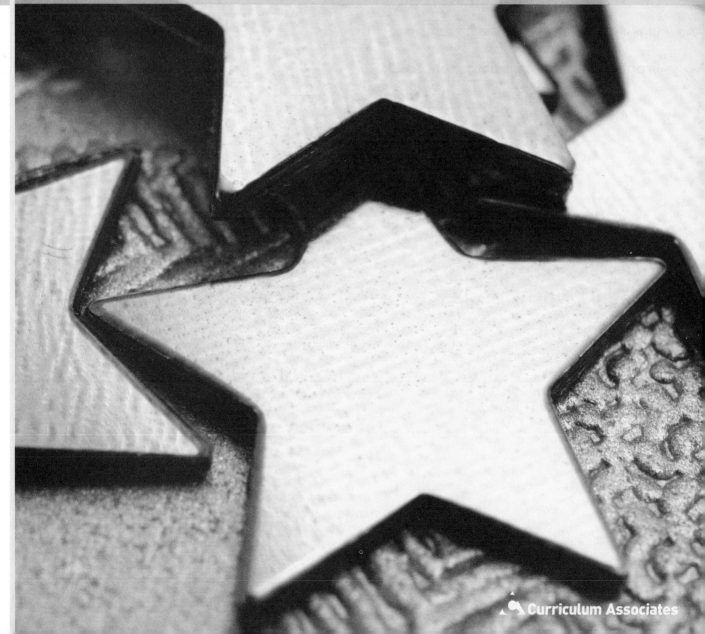

Curriculum Associates

ACKNOWLEDGMENTS

Product Development

Developer and Author: Deborah Adcock

Editor

Robert G. Forest Ed.D.

Design

Cover Designer: Matt Pollock

Book Designer: Pat Lucas

Illustration/Photography Credit

Illustrator: Jim Roldan

Front cover, title page: iStockphoto LP

ISBN 978-0-7609-6362-3

©2010, 2009—Curriculum Associates, LLC
North Billerica, MA 01862

TABLE OF CONTENTS

Lesson 1   Finding Main Idea 4

Lesson 2   Finding Details 14

Lessons 1-2   REVIEW 24

Lesson 3   Putting Ideas in Order 26

Lesson 4   Understanding What Happens and Why 36

Lessons 3-4   REVIEW 46

Lesson 5   Making a Guess 48

Lesson 6   Figuring Things Out 58

Lessons 5-6   REVIEW 68

Lessons 1-6   FINAL REVIEW 70

Draw a picture of **a rainy day.**

The main idea of the picture is **a rainy day.**

Draw a picture of **a boy flying a kite.**

The picture is mostly about **a boy flying a kite.**

Work with a Partner

What is the picture mostly about?

A   a girl sitting in the sand

B   a bird flying in the sky

C   a sunny day at the beach

Look at this picture.

What is the main idea of the picture?

A   The duck walks.

B   The duck swims.

C   The duck flies.

1. What is the main idea of the picture?

   A The man digs.

   B The man sleeps.

   C The man runs.

2. What is the main idea of the picture?

   A Mary washes a dish.

   B Mary washes the car.

   C Mary washes the dog.

The baby crawls.

A

B

C

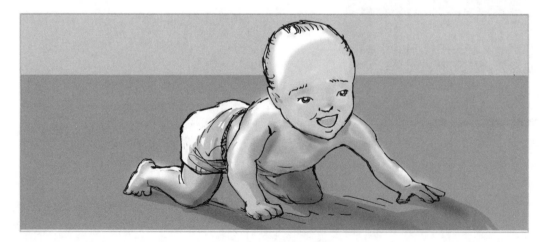

3. What is the main idea of the picture?

    A   The rabbit eats a carrot.

    B   The rabbit sees a cat.

    C   The rabbit digs a hole.

4. What is the main idea of the picture?

    A   Tom climbs the tree.

    B   Tom opens the door.

    C   Tom rakes the leaves.

Look at this picture.
Think about the main idea of the picture.

Read this story. Think about the main idea of the story.

> Kayla enjoys winter. She likes to play
> in the snow. Sometimes Kayla makes
> snowmen. She also builds forts.

Look at this picture. Then read the story.

Patty washes King every Saturday. She fills a tub with water and gives her dog a bath. King enjoys being clean.

5. The main idea of the story is

   A   Patty fills a tub.

   B   Patty feeds her dog.

   C   Patty washes King every Saturday.

Look at this picture. Then read the story.

Paul got some paint. Then he got a brush. Paul is painting the fence.

6. The main idea of the story is

   A   Paul is fixing the fence.

   B   Paul is painting the fence.

   C   Paul is cleaning the fence.

Read this story. Think about the main idea.

Lori does not feel well. She did not go to school. She stayed in bed all day. She drew pictures. She read books. Tomorrow, Lori will feel better.

7. The picture shows that
A   Lori is sick.
B   Lori goes to school.
C   Lori feels better.

8. What is the main idea of the story?
A   Lori draws pictures.
B   Lori does not feel well.
C   Lori reads books.

Read this story. Think about the main idea.

Ted is very small. He lives in a large glass tank. He moves slowly. He can pull his head into his shell. Ted is my pet turtle.

9. The story is mostly about
   A a pet turtle.
   B a large shell.
   C a glass tank.

10. What is a good name for the story?
   A "Moving Slowly"
   B "The Turtle's Shell"
   C "Ted the Turtle"

Add some details to the picture.

Add some details to the picture.

 Work with a Partner

What is the most important
idea in the picture?

A   The girl is happy.

B   The girl is sad.

C   The girl is sleepy.

Which of these is a detail
in the picture?

A   the sun

B   the stars

C   the rain

Look at this picture.

What is the main idea of the picture?

A   Jake mixes.

B   Jake cleans.

C   Jake eats.

What is Jake making?

A   eggs

B   cookies

C   sandwiches

Which detail in the picture helps you figure out what Jake is making?

A   the bowl

B   the egg

C   the box

1. The puppy is
   A   afraid.
   B   hurt.
   C   tired.

2. The mouse is
   A   wet.
   B   hungry.
   C   noisy.

Look at the picture.

3. The boy lost his

A   friend.

B   balloon.

C   money.

Finding Details

Look at the picture.

4. Where is Mrs. Wong?

    A   at the park
    B   at her front door
    C   inside her house

Look at the picture. Think about the details in the picture.

Read this story. Think about the details in the story.

> Ana just finished breakfast. Now she is getting ready to leave for school. The bus is waiting for her. Ana needs to hurry!

Look at the picture. Then read the story.

Fluffy is my cat. Fluffy likes to play.

5. What is one detail in the picture?

A a cozy bed

B a bowl of food

C a ball of yarn

Look at the picture. Then read the story.

Maya and Grandpa go to the lake every Saturday. They sail across the lake in Grandpa's boat. Maya likes to sail.

6. What are two details in the picture?

A a lake and a boat

B a kite and the sun

C a plane and some clouds

Read this story. Think about the details.

Oak trees have leaves. The leaves are green in the spring. The leaves change color in the fall. They get dry and fall to the ground.

7. The story is mostly about

A colors.

B spring.

C leaves.

8. When do oak leaves change color?

A in the spring

B in the fall

C in the summer

Read this story. Think about the details.

Su and Ray went to the pet store. Su liked the birds. Ray liked the puppies. They both liked the rabbits.

9. Where did Su and Ray go?

A to the zoo

B to the market

C to the pet store

10. What did Su and Ray both like?

A puppies

B rabbits

C birds

Read this story. Then answer the questions.

A lion was asleep under a tree. A mouse ran across his back. The lion woke up angry. The lion grabbed the mouse.

"Do not hurt me!" the mouse cried. "One day I will help you." The lion laughed and let the mouse go.

One morning the mouse heard the lion cry out for help. The mouse ran to see what was the matter. The lion was trapped in a net. The mouse chewed on the ropes. Soon the lion was free. The lion and the mouse became best friends.

Finding Main Idea

1. What is the main idea of the picture?

   A   A mouse wakes up a lion.

   B   A mouse runs across a lion's back.

   C   A mouse begs not to be eaten.

Finding Main Idea

2. The story is mostly about

   A   a mouse that wakes a lion.

   B   a lion that is helped by a mouse.

   C   a lion that is trapped in a net.

Finding Main Idea

3. What is a good name for the story?

   A   "New Friends"

   B   "The Angry Lion"

   C   "King of the Beasts"

Finding Details

4. In the picture, the lion is sleeping under a

   A   bridge.

   B   rock.

   C   tree.

Finding Details

5. The lion was caught in a

   A   hole.

   B   net.

   C   box.

Finding Details

6. The mouse chewed on the

   A   tree.

   B   leaves.

   C   ropes.

✏ **Draw the last thing you did before you went to bed last night.**

✏ **Draw the first thing you did after you got out of bed this morning.**

Work with a Partner

Look at the pictures.

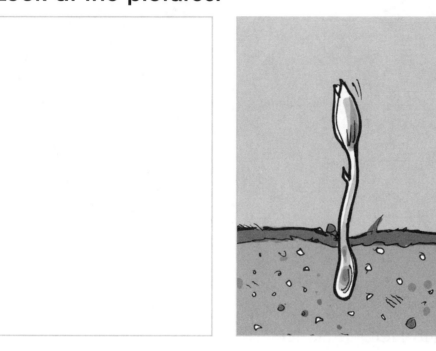

Find the picture that belongs in the first box.

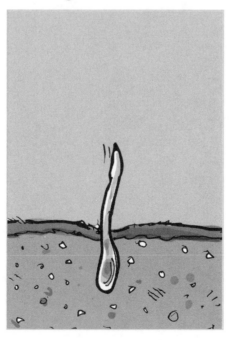

A   B   C

1

2

3

Which picture shows what happens last?

A   1

B   2

C   3

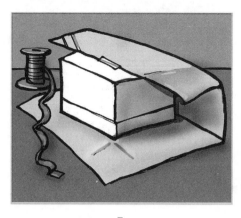

1

2

3

1. Which picture comes first?

A 1

B 2

C 3

1

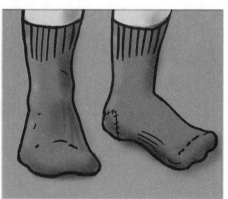

2

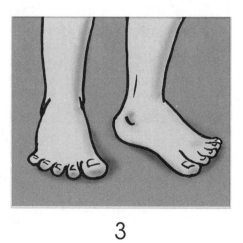

3

2. Which picture comes second?

A 1

B 2

C 3

Read this story. Then look at the pictures.

Toby's Bath

First, Matt puts water in the tub.

Next, Matt puts soap in the tub.

Then Matt puts Toby in the tub.

1

2

3

Which picture shows what Matt will do second?

A   1

B   2

C   3

Look at the pictures.

1

2

3

3. What is the correct order of the story parts?

    A   3, 2, 1

    B   2, 3, 1

    C   1, 2, 3

Look at the pictures.

1

2

3

4. What is the correct order of the story parts?

    A   3, 2, 1

    B   2, 1, 3

    C   1, 2, 3

Look at the pictures.

Read this story. Think about the order of ideas as you read.

The first thing Iris will do is make her bed.
After she makes her bed, she will wash her
bike. Next, Iris will water the plants before
she feeds her goldfish.

Look at the pictures. Then read the story.

On Monday, Ava has piano lessons. On Wednesday, Ava plays soccer. On Saturday, she goes swimming.

5. When will Ava play soccer?

A   Monday

B   Saturday

C   Wednesday

Look at the pictures. Then read the story.

Mr. Brown baked a cake. He frosted the cake when it was cool. He put candles on top when he was done.

6. What did Mr. Brown do second?

A   He baked the cake.

B   He frosted the cake.

C   He put candles on the cake.

Read this story. Think about the order of ideas.

Will got dressed as fast as he could. Next, he put on his coat and ran outside. Then he went to the park to play with his friends.

7. What did Will do after he ran outside?

   A He got dressed.

   B He put on his coat.

   C He went to the park.

8. Which clue word tells what Will did second?

   A first

   B next

   C then

Read this story. Think about the order of ideas.

The sun was bright all morning. Clouds filled the sky in the afternoon. It rained all night.

9. When did clouds fill the sky?
  A   in the morning
  B   in the afternoon
  C   at night

10. What happened after clouds filled the sky?
  A   It rained.
  B   The sun came out.
  C   The sky got bright.

✏️ **Draw what a flower looks like when it gets enough water.**

✏️ **Draw what a flower looks like when it does not get enough water.**

Work with a Partner

Why was there a pull on Jim's fishing line?

A   Jim caught some seaweed.

B   Jim caught a big fish.

C   Jim's line got stuck in the rocks.

Look at the picture.

1

2

3

Which picture shows why the snowman is melting?

A   1

B   2

C   3

1. Why does Zach need an umbrella?

    A   It is raining.

    B   It is dark.

    C   It is cold.

2. What happened to the window?

    A   A bat broke it.

    B   A bird broke it.

    C   A ball broke it.

Look at the picture. The picture shows what happened.

What happened?

A   The table fell over.

B   The lamp fell over.

C   The vase fell over.

Look at the picture.

3. What happened to Tim?

    A   Tim got an A on his test.

    B   Tim did not do well on his test.

    C   Tim forgot to study for his test.

Look at the picture.

4. Why did this happen?

    A   Tim watched a lot of TV.

    B   Tim played with his friends.

    C   Tim studied for his test.

Look at the picture.

Read this story. Think about what happened and why.

Gina went for a ride on her bike. Gina was
not watching the road, so she hit a rock.
Because she hit the rock, her bike tipped over.
Gina fell to the ground.

Look at the picture.

5. What happened?

    A The bird flew away.

    B The bird ate all its food.

    C The bird drank all its water.

Look at the picture.

6. Owen cannot swim with his sister because

    A he does not know how to swim.

    B he does not have a bathing suit.

    C he does not feel well.

Read this story. Think about what happens and why.

A cat walked through the kitchen and saw a mouse. The cat chased the mouse. The mouse was afraid, so it ran into a small hole in the wall. Since the cat was too big, it could not fit through the hole. The mouse was safe—for now!

7. What clue word tells why the mouse ran into the hole?

   A so

   B if

   C since

8. The cat could not fit through the hole because the cat

   A was too small.

   B was too big.

   C was too slow.

Read this story. Think about what happens and why.

Dad and Ella needed milk, so they drove to the store. The car made a loud sound. Then the car stopped moving. "Oops," Dad said. "I forgot to put gas in the car."

9. What happened after the car made a loud sound?

A   Dad and Ella bought milk.

B   The car stopped moving.

C   Dad and Ella drove to the store.

10. Why did the car stop moving?

A   Dad forgot to buy milk.

B   Dad forgot how to drive.

C   Dad forgot to put gas in the car.

Look at the picture.

On Monday, Jack said, "I will teach my dog to fetch because it will be fun"

On Tuesday, Max learned to fetch Jack's sneakers. On Wednesday, Max learned to fetch Jack's coat. On Thursday, Max learned to fetch Jack's hat.

On Friday, Jack went outside to get the newspaper. But Max had already fetched the paper. He had fetched all the neighbors' newspapers, too! Poor Jack. He had to spend all morning putting the newspapers back.

Putting Ideas in Order

1. In the story, clues that tell about order are

   A times of day.

   B months of the year.

   C days of the week.

Putting Ideas in Order

2. When did Jack decide to teach Max tricks?

   A Monday

   B Friday

   C Saturday

Putting Ideas in Order

3. Which of these did Max learn first?

   A to get Jack's coat

   B to get Jack's sneakers

   C to get Jack's hat

Understanding What Happens and Why

4. Why did Jack return the newspapers?

   A Jack's job was to deliver them to his neighbors.

   B Max had fetched them from all Jack's neighbors.

   C Someone brought them to the wrong house.

Understanding What Happens and Why

5. Why did Jack teach Max to fetch?

   A Jack thought it would be fun.

   B Jack needed help with his chores.

   C Jack was too busy to do things himself.

Understanding What Happens and Why

6. Which clue word tells why Jack taught Max tricks?

   A so

   B since

   C because

PART ONE: Think About the Strategy

✏ **Draw your answer.**

✏ **Draw your answer.**

Work with a Partner

Look at the pictures.

1

2

3

Which picture shows what Jenna sees?

A   1

B   2

C   3

Look at the pictures.

What will Jenna do next?

A   give her pictures away

B   put her pictures in a book

C   plan another trip to the zoo

1. What will Carlos do next?
   A   go for a walk
   B   go for a run
   C   go roller skating

2. What will Eve do next?
   A   write a story
   B   paint a picture
   C   play a game

Look at the pictures. The pictures tell about Bob.

What will Bob do next?

A   visit a friend

B   go for a bike ride

C   put the food away

3. Make a guess about a character that might be in the book, *The Toad and the Giant.*

   A   an elf

   B   a teacher

   C   a bus driver

4. Make a guess about the title of Eric's book.

   A   "Dooley Goes to School"

   B   "You Can Do it, Dooley"

   C   "Dooley's Big Idea"

Look at the pictures.

Read this story. Think about what will happen next.

Alex always keeps his eyes on the ground. He finds all kinds of treasures by keeping his head down when he walks.

Today, Alex found a nickel on his way to school. But watch out, Alex! You need to remember to look up once in a while.

Read this story.

Mike has packed a suitcase. Now he is driving to the airport.

5. What will happen next?

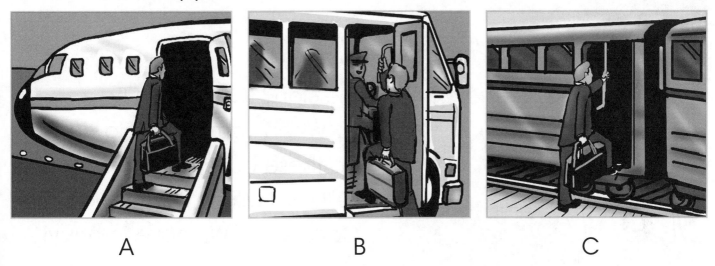

A   B   C

Read this story.

Jayne is tired. She puts on her pajamas. Then she washes her face and brushes her teeth.

6. What will happen next?

A   B   C

Read this story. Think about what will happen next.

Carla is putting candles on a cake. Ty is blowing up balloons.

"Are you going to hang up the sign?" Carla asks Ty.

"When I am done blowing up these balloons," Ty says.

"Mom will be home soon," Carla says. "We have to hurry!"

7. Make a guess about what Ty and Carla are doing.

   A   planning a birthday party

   B   getting ready for a party with friends

   C   making dinner for their family

8. Make a guess about how Mom will feel when she gets home.

   A   sad

   B   surprised

   C   upset

Read this story. Think about what will happen next.

Who Is Big and Who Is Little?

"Look at me! I am big," says Ant.

"No, I am big," says Bird. "You are little."

"I am big," says Dog to Ant and Bird. "You both are little."

Horse shakes his head and laughs.

9. What will Horse say?

   A "None of us are big. We are all little."

   B "None of you are little. I am big."

   C "I am big. You are all little."

10. The title of the story helps you make a guess about

   A how the story will end.

   B what the story is about.

   C who is in the story.

✏ **Draw your answer.**

✏ **Draw your answer.**

Work with a Partner

Look at the pictures.

A

B

C

Look at the picture.

You can tell that Tess and her friends are

A   playing at the park.

B   cleaning the park.

C   having a picnic at the park.

Look at the picture.

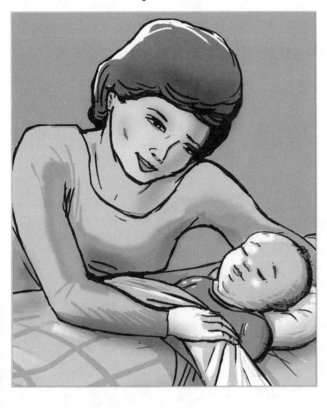

1. Mom put a blanket over the baby. Mom probably thought the baby was

   A warm.

   B cold.

   C hot.

Look at the picture.

2. Dad called Ming to the table. It was probably time to

   A eat.

   B study.

   C clean.

Look at the pictures. The pictures tell about Jamal.

You can tell that Jamal is

A   visiting his neighbor.

B   shopping for a toy.

C   having a yard sale.

3. You can tell that
- A summer is coming.
- B spring is coming.
- C winter is coming.

4. You can tell that the eggs
- A fell from the nest.
- B are about to hatch.
- C belong to a turtle.

Look at the pictures.

Read this story. Think about what the details tell you.

James wakes up every day at 6:00 A.M. He always gets dressed right away. Next, James makes breakfast. He eats the same thing each morning—oatmeal, fruit, and orange juice.

Read this story.

I am found on your face.
I help keep dirt out of your eyes.
Tears will make me wet.
What am I?

5.

A

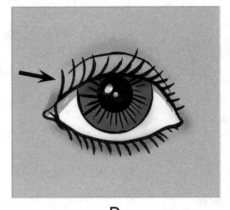
B

C

Read this story.

Haley takes a seat. The smell of popcorn
fills the air. The lights go down. The screen
comes alive. Haley smiles.

6.

A

B

C

Read this story. Then answer the questions.

Some animals like to steal bird eggs. Snakes are one such animal. They crack the eggs open and eat what is inside. Mother birds watch for animals that might harm their eggs.

A mother robin needs to leave her nest to get some food. But there is something she must do before she leaves.

7. What will the robin probably do before she leaves her nest?
   A find some worms to eat
   B put her eggs in another nest
   C look for animals that might harm her eggs

8. Which of these is probably true?
   A Birds eat snakes.
   B All animals steal eggs.
   C Birds are afraid of snakes.

**Read this story.
Then answer the questions.**

Peaches and Cream

The children in Mr. Lee's class have two pet hamsters. One is orange. Her name is Peaches. The other hamster is light brown. Her name is Cream.

Students take turns caring for Peaches and Cream on weekends. This weekend, Paulo will take care of the pets. In two weeks, Joy will have her turn.

9. You can tell that

A Mr. Lee takes the pets home during the week.

B a different student takes care of the pets each weekend.

C Joy is taking care of the pets this weekend.

10. Peaches and Cream probably got their names because of

A how they look.

B what they eat.

C where they live.

Read this story. Then answer the questions.

David and Jay were best friends. Then Nate moved next door to Jay. Nate and Jay spent all their time together. David was left out. He had no one to play with.

One day, Nate told Jay that he was going on vacation. "I will be gone for two weeks," he said.

"What will I do without Nate?" Jay wondered. Then he thought about his old friend David. He felt bad about not spending time with him. Nate would return in two weeks. Jay would make sure they all played together from now on.

Jay phoned David. "Do you want to play?" he asked.

David was quiet for a long time. Jay held his breath. Finally, David said, "I would like that." Then he added, "But is there something you want to say to me first?"

Making a Guess

1. Make a guess about what David wants Jay to say.

   A "Let's play."

   B "I am sorry."

   C "Are you busy?"

Making a Guess

2. What will probably happen next?

   A Jay will tell David he does not want to play.

   B Nate will return from vacation.

   C David and Jay will spend time together.

Making a Guess

3. Which clue helps you answer question 2?

   A David had no one to play with.

   B Jay was going on vacation.

   C David said, "I would like that."

Figuring Things Out

4. You can tell that

   A David and Jay used to play together all the time.

   B David no longer wants to be friends with Jay.

   C David does not care about Jay's feelings.

Figuring Things Out

5. What will probably happen when Nate returns?

   A Jay will forget about David.

   B David, Nate, and Jay will all play together.

   C David and Nate will play without Jay.

Figuring Things Out

6. What detail from the story helped you answer question 5?

   A Jay held his breath.

   B Nate would return in two weeks.

   C Jay would make sure the three boys played together.

Read this story about Tara.
Then answer questions about the story.
Choose the best answer for Numbers 1 through 6.

Tara likes plants. She also likes the color yellow. She planted some seeds for yellow flowers. She planted the seeds in a pot by her front door.

Every day Tara checked her seeds. She made sure they had lots of sun. She watered them when they were dry. Soon green plants grew. Then yellow flowers bloomed.

One day while Tara was at school, a robin rested on the flower pot. The bird had seeds in its mouth. Some of the seeds fell into the pot.

A few weeks later, Tara saw two red flowers growing in her pot of yellow flowers. Tara scratched her head. "How did the red flowers get there?" she wondered. Tara was going to pull the red flowers out of the pot. But then she saw how pretty they looked.

Finding Main Idea

1. The story is mostly about

   A   a girl who likes plants.

   B   a girl who planted flower seeds.

   C   a girl who likes the color yellow.

Understanding What Happens and Why

4. Why did Tara give her seeds water?

   A   because they were green

   B   because they were dry

   C   because they were not growing

Finding Details

2. Where did Tara keep her pot of flowers?

   A   by the front door

   B   near a window

   C   on the back porch

Making a Guess

5. What will Tara probably do about the red flowers?

   A   She will leave them in the pot.

   B   She will pull them out of the pot.

   C   She will give them to her mother.

Putting Ideas in Order

3. Which of these happened last?

   A   Yellow flowers bloomed.

   B   A bird rested on the pot.

   C   Tara planted some seeds.

Figuring Things Out

6. You can tell that the red flowers came from

   A   the seeds Tara planted.

   B   the green plants that grew.

   C   the seeds that the robin dropped.

**Read this letter that Ida wrote to her cousin.
Then answer questions about the letter.
Choose the best answer for Numbers 1 through 6.**

Dear Rob,

   April vacation is almost here. I am counting the days until you visit. I am so glad that we have a whole week to spend together.

   Dad is taking us to a circus on Sunday. On Monday, Mom is taking us to the movies. On Tuesday, we will visit Uncle Sam in the city. On Wednesday, there is a concert at the park. Then on Thursday, Mom is taking us to Pebble Island. There are no roads to the island. We have to ride in a boat to get there! Pebble Island has the best playground. We will pack a picnic lunch and play all afternoon. Our week together will be such fun!

                              Your cousin,

                              Ida

Finding Main Idea

1. What is the main idea of the letter?

   A   Two cousins like to have fun.

   B   A girl is excited about her cousin's visit.

   C   There is always a lot to do on vacation.

Finding Details

2. Rob will visit Ida for

   A   one day.

   B   one week.

   C   one month.

Putting Ideas in Order

3. Where will Rob and Ida go on Monday?

   A   to the circus

   B   to the movies

   C   to a concert

Understanding What Happens and Why

4. Rob and Ida will ride in a boat because

   A   it is the only way to get to a circus.

   B   it is the only thing to do on vacation.

   C   it is the only way to reach Pebble Island.

Making a Guess

5. Which of these will most likely happen?

   A   Rob and Ida will have fun together.

   B   Rob will decide he does not want to visit Ida.

   C   There will be nothing for Rob and Ida to do on vacation.

Figuring Things Out

6. You can tell that Rob will visit Ida during the

   A   fall.

   B   winter.

   C   spring.

Read this story about Li.
Then answer questions about the story.
Choose the best answer for Numbers 1 through 6.

Li was at the pond fishing. He felt a tug on his line. He thought he had caught a big fish. But all he caught was a big plant.

Li looked at the plant on his hook. He saw something on the leaves. It looked like jelly. Li took the plant off his hook. He dropped it into his fishing bucket with a splash.

Days later, Li was cleaning the garage. He was about to wash out his fishing bucket. He saw the plant floating at the top. He also saw something else in the water. Ten little tadpoles were swimming about. They were already starting to look like frogs.

"That jelly must have been frog eggs," Li said. "I must get these guys back to the pond."

Finding Main Idea

1. What is a good title for the story?

   A "A Surprise for Li"

   B "How Frogs Grow"

   C "Fishing for Frogs"

Finding Details

2. Where did Li put the plant he caught?

   A in the pond

   B in his bucket

   C on his hook

Putting Ideas in Order

3. When did Li clean the garage?

   A before he went fishing

   B after he went fishing

   C the day he went fishing

Understanding What Happens and Why

4. Why did Li think he had caught a big fish?

   A He heard a splash in the water.

   B He felt a tug on his line.

   C He saw something on his hook.

Making a Guess

5. What will Li do next?

   A go fishing

   B look for frogs

   C return the tadpoles to the pond

Figuring Things Out

6. You can tell that frog eggs

   A look like fish.

   B look like leaves.

   C look like jelly.

Read this fairy tale about three pigs.
Then answer questions about the fairy tale.
Choose the best answer for Numbers 1 through 6.

The Three Pigs

Once upon a time, there were three sad pigs. It had not rained in a long time. Their mud puddle had dried up.

One day, the first pig said, "I miss our mud puddle."

"Me too," said the second pig. "Maybe we should make our own mud puddle. But where will we get the water?"

The third pig said, "Let's tell each other sad stories. Then we will catch our tears in a pail until we have enough water."

The other pigs laughed at such a silly idea. They laughed so hard that tears came out of their eyes. Then they told the silly idea to their pig friends. Their friends laughed so hard that tears came out of their eyes, too.

While all the other pigs were laughing, the third pig got busy. He caught all their tears in a pail. Soon he had enough water for the three pigs to make a fine mud puddle for themselves. And they lived happily ever after, even though their pig friends were no longer laughing.

Finding Main Idea

1. Another good name for the fairy tale is

   A "The Silly Idea."

   B "A Puddle of Tears."

   C "No Rain Today."

Finding Details

2. What was the third pig's idea?

   A to catch tears in a pail

   B to laugh really hard

   C to try and make it rain

Putting Ideas in Order

3. Which of these happened first?

   A The pigs were all laughing.

   B The third pig had an idea.

   C The first pig said, "I miss our mud puddle."

Understanding What Happens and Why

4. What happened because there was no rain?

   A The pigs had no food.

   B The pigs had no place to live.

   C The pigs had no mud puddle.

Making a Guess

5. What will most likely happen the next time the third pig has an idea?

   A The other pigs will laugh.

   B The other pigs will listen.

   C The other pigs will cry.

Figuring Things Out

6. The pigs' friends probably stopped laughing because

   A they did not know how to make a mud puddle.

   B they did not want to make more tears.

   C the third pig's idea worked.